G000136392

What's What

STAR WARS®

EPISODE I™

What's What

by Daniel Wallace

RUNNING PRESS
PHILADELPHIA · LONDON

A Running Press Miniature Edition™

© 1999 Lucasfilm Ltd. & TM
All rights reserved. Used under authorization.
All rights reserved under the Pan-American
and International Copyright Conventions.

Printed in China

This book may not be reproduced in whole or in part,
in any form or by any means, electronic or mechanical, including
photocopying, recording, or by any information
storage and retrieval system now known or hereafter invented,
without written permission from the publisher.

The proprietary trade dress, including the size and format,
of this Running Press Miniature Edition™ is the property
of Running Press. It may not be used or reproduced
without the express written permission of Running Press.
Library of Congress Cataloging-in-Publication Number
98-67643

ISBN 0-7624-0520-1

This book may be ordered by mail from the publisher.
Please include $1.00 for postage and handling.
But try your bookstore first!

Running Press Book Publishers
125 South Twenty-second Street
Philadelphia, Pennsylvania 19103-4399

Visit us on the web!
www.runningpress.com

Contents

Introduction

WHAT'S A WOOKIEE?

It wasn't too many years ago that no one except George Lucas knew the answer to that question. His early drafts for his heroic new space fantasy, *The Star Wars*, were stuffed with bizarre and inscrutable terms such as bantha, blaster, Mos Eisley, and astro-droid. But audiences were enthralled. The exotic vocabulary lent credence to the notion that this was an actual world with its own believable set of rules. Almost immediately, *Star Wars* became a global phenomenon and Chewbacca, the world's most famous Wookiee, an indelible pop-culture icon.

Now, twenty-two years after the debut of *Star Wars: A New Hope*, it's all starting again. Episode I is the first chapter in the unfolding *Star Wars* saga, and all the elements that made the original films into cinematic classics are here. Fantastic environments like Jedi temples and under-water bubble cities. Creatures and monsters more outlandish than anything conceived in the most vivid daydream. Starships, weapons, and automatons, each very familiar in design yet still subtly "old-fashioned," being a full generation removed from the styles seen in the classic trilogy.

So don't worry if you can't yet tell a shakk from a STAP, or a pit droid from a peko peko. At last the world is being reintroduced to the extraordinary realm of *Star Wars*. If you want to be an instant expert, this book is a good place to start.

SHIPS AND

VEHICLES

Trade Federation Battleship

The wealthy and influential Trade Federation enforces its heavy-handed policies with an armada of unmistakable and extremely menacing **battleships**. Bristling with weaponry, the huge vessels are also heavily shielded. The Trade Federation uses some modified battleships, called droid control ships, to coordinate their droid armies.

The Corellian-built *Radiant VII*, carrying the Jedi Obi-Wan Kenobi and Qui-Gon Jinn, was personally dispatched to the blockaded planet Naboo by Supreme Chancellor Valorum. The *Radiant VII's* cluster of communications antennae allows the ship to communicate with anyone, while its bright red hull indicates its protected diplomatic status.

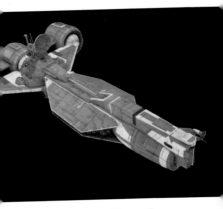

Republic Cruiser

TRADE FEDERATION
LARGE TRANSPORT
(MTT)

The Trade Federation's formidable **Multi Troop Transport**, or **MTT**, is a hovering repulsorlift vehicle that ferries Trade

Federation battle droids and destroyer droids into active combat zones. Heavily armored against attack, the MTT has four laser cannons and an internal transport rack on which 112 folded battle droids are stored.

Single Trooper Aerial Platform (STAP)

The **Single Trooper Aerial Platform (STAP)** is a lightweight hovercraft built to transport individual battle droids. STAPs are typically dispatched ahead of the main army as battlefield reconnaissance scouts or used as anti-personnel hunters to mop up small targets with their twin blaster cannons.

Trade Federation
Battle Tank (AAT)

The mightiest fortifications crumble when assaulted by a Trade Federation battle tank, also known as an **Armored Attack Tank** or **AAT**. A product of the Baktoid Armor Workshop, each tank carries a crew of four battle droids and is armed with five laser guns and six energy shell launchers.

GUNGAN SUB

*T*he amphibious Gungans use squid-like "bongos" as common underwater transports. The strange submersible vehicles are propelled by rotating tentacles powered by an electromotive field motor. Their organically grown hulls are durable, but are no match for the fangs of Naboo's gigantic sea monsters.

The Naboo Queer

Sleek, elegant, and breathtaking, the transport vessel used by Queen Amidala of Naboo is a handcrafted J-type ship powered by a 327 Nubian engine, specially crafted for the young monarch on the planet Nubia. In keeping with the peaceful nature of the Naboo people, the Queen's ship has no weapons, only deflector shields.

Royal Starship

30

The **Naboo Royal N-1 starfighter** is a nimble one-person craft flown by the volunteer Royal Naboo Security Forces. Yellow-colored and trimmed with royal chrome, each fighter is armed with twin blaster cannons and a cache of proton torpedoes. An astromech droid behind the cockpit helps the pilot monitor flight performance.

Naboo Starfighter

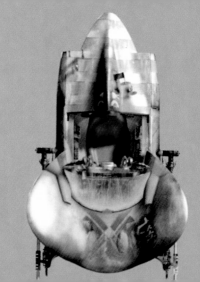

ANAKIN SKYWALKER'S PODRACER

Resembling beast-drawn chariots from days of old, Podracers consist of small cockpits towed behind enormous jet engines. Anakin Skywalker's custom-built **Podracer** has a smooth contoured shape and two souped-up Radon-Ulzer Podengines with scoop-air stabilizers. Multiple air brakes allow Anakin to slow down his hotrod in a hurry.

*T*he arrogant alien Sebulba pilots a dagger-shaped racer that has the sleek appearance of a starfighter. Illegal flame throwers mounted on the split-X Podengines lie ready to cook unwary competitors. Like many **Podracers**, Sebulba's dragster can reach speeds well over 800 kilometers per hour.

SEBULBA'S PODRACER

Sith Infiltrator

Darth Maul's **Sith Infiltrator** is a customized Star Courier design incorporating six laser cannons, a sophisticated tracking system, and a cloaking device that can render the ship invisible. Its powerful ion drive system employs folding radiator panels that retract during planetary landings.

SITH
SPEEDER

The **Sith speeder** has no weapons, sensors, or shields—only an immensely powerful repulsorlift engine making it capable of astonishing speed and maneuverability. The speeder is Darth Maul's preferred means of transportation since it allows him to swoop down on his foes and quickly dispatch them with his lightsaber.

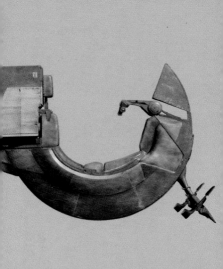

Coruscant Air Taxi

Coruscant, one of the most overcrowded planets in the galaxy, employs a fleet of **air taxis** to ferry its citizens from one skyscraper to the next. The largest of these vessels have multiple decks and can hold more than 1000 passengers.

FLASH

*T*he Royal Naboo Security Forces use the **Flash speeder** for street patrolling and high-speed pursuit. The speeder seats only two, but two additional soldiers can ride on the back. Flash speeders are outfitted with light blaster cannons.

SPEEDER

GIAN SPEEDER

The **Gian speeder** is more heavily armed than the Flash speeder and better suited for crowd control and urban defense. The two side-mounted blasters are standard; security and police models have an additional heavy strike cannon mounted on the hood. Command speeders come equipped with holographic projection systems.

44

Lethal Trade Federation war machines such as MTTs, AATs, and STAPs can't get to the surface of a soon-to-be-subjugated planet without an immense armored carrier. The **Trade Federation landing craft** holds thousands of battle droids and dozens of pieces of heavy equipment. Its unique double-wing design provides stability during rapid atmospheric descents.

TRADE FEDERATION
LANDING CRAFT

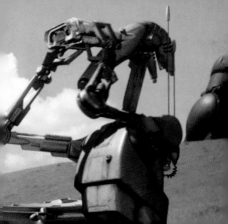

BATTLE DROID

*T*he foot soldiers of the Trade Federation Army, **battle droids** overwhelm their enemies through coordinated tactics and sheer force of numbers. All battle droids are controlled from a remote command source. Specialized types are distinguished by color—yellow markings for commanders, blue for pilots, and maroon for security guards.

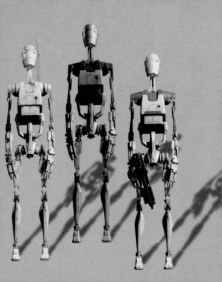

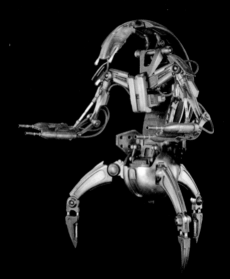

Also known as wheel droids, heavy-hitting **destroyer droids** are elite and deadly combat machines. They move into position in an armored "wheel" configuration and then unfold to become terrifying weapons platforms. They have laser cannons in place of arms and can generate their own deflector shields.

Destroyer Droid

TRADE FEDERATION DROID STARFIGHTER

A battleship hangar filled with **Trade Federation droid starfighters** resembles a nightmarish aviary of predatory hawk-bats. The birdlike fighter craft are actually oversized droids, engineered to operate in atmosphere and deep space. Each droid has weapons compartments that slide open to reveal hull-puncturing laser cannons.

Protocol Droid

The TC **protocol** series is a popular line of diplomatic and translation **droids** manufactured by Cybot Galactica. TC droids are prized for their unflappable poise in even the least dignified situation. The units are quite expensive and are frequently seen in the company of Galactic senators and Trade Federation officials.

ASTROMECH DROID

Industrial Automaton's R2 **astromech droids** are perfectly suited for starship maintenance. Many are used by the Royal House of Naboo as in-flight counterparts for the N-1 starfighter. All Naboo astromechs are fitted with repulsorlifts and maneuvering jets to assist in performing emergency extravehicular repairs.

Podracers are notoriously difficult to fix and maintain, so most speedways have pit areas for in-race repairs. **Pit droids** are cheap, durable mechanics that can lift many times their own weight. The droids are deployed in swarms in order to make the most out of each pit stop.

PIT DROID

Sith Probe Droid

Sith **"dark eye" probe droids** are cunning spies that move in the shadows and attack on the sly. Each floating orb has sharp, long-range sensors and an internal weapons mount for affixing deadly devices. Darth Maul can control up to six of the droids with his wristband comlink.

EQUIPMENT

Jedi Lightsaber

No weapon is more distinctive or respected than the **lightsaber**. The age-old energy blade is virtually synonymous with the order of Jedi Knights. Many lightsabers from this era lack flashback waterseals and can be shorted out if submerged while the blade is ignited.

DARTH
MAUL'S
LIGHTSABER

Darth Maul's lightsaber has energy blades that ignite from both ends of the handle. Wielding this difficult weapon requires a radically different fighting style, and Darth Maul is a master of this esoteric and deadly art.

GUNGAN
ELECTROPOLE

Both a ceremonial object and a defensive weapon, the **electropole** is carried by Gungan perimeter guards while they patrol the city astride their kaadu steeds. The weapon's tip generates a concentrated electrical charge that can stun intruders and drive off unfriendly sealife.

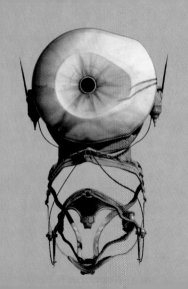

Gungan Shield Generator

Carried into battle by stu **rdy** fambaas, **Gungan shield generators** create a blaster-proof canopy. When se**veral** of the devices are used simultaneous**ly**, they link together to form an energy um**brella** that can protect an entire army. Th**e** shield is impervious to laser fire but **can** be penetrated by small slow-movi**ng** objects.

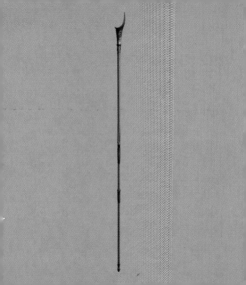

GUNGAN

Although not as powerful as an energy ball catapult, the **cesta** gives individual Gungan soldiers a useful weapon for ranged combat. The end of the staff cradles a small energy ball that is forcefully hurled into enemy lines. In close quarters, the cesta doubles as a quarterstaff.

CESTA

Mechno-chair

Mechno-chairs are meant to convey a sense of lordly grandeur, but they often say more about their owners' idleness and decadence. The expensive contraptions are individually assembled by Neimoidian specialty artisans.

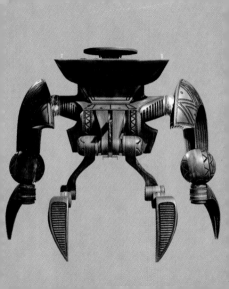

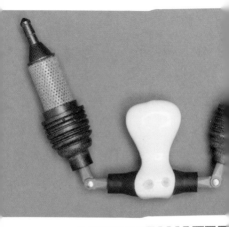

UNDERWATER

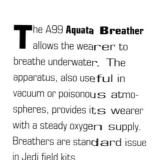

The A99 **Aquata Breather** allows the wearer to breathe underwater. The apparatus, also useful in vacuum or poisonous atmospheres, provides its wearer with a steady oxygen supply. Breathers are standard issue in Jedi field kits.

REATHING DEVICE

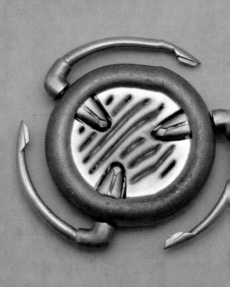

Jedi Holoprojector

Jedi Knights often carry hand-held **holographic projectors** for reproducing three-dimensional images. Holograms can be recorded and then redisplayed, or they can be loaded directly from the device's built-in image library. When used in conjunction with a Jedi comlink, the holoprojector relays real-time holographic messages.

JEDI TESTING SCREEN

Mastery of the Force requires years of practice, but even a novice Jedi can tap into the Force on an unconscious level. To verify these potential Knights, the Jedi Council employs a datapad-sized **testing screen**. The device flashes a series of unrelated images faster than the unaided eye can follow.

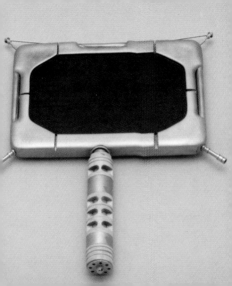

CREATURES

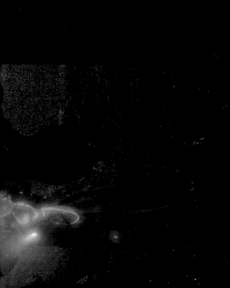

*T*o many observers, Gungans and kaadu seem to be an almost inseparable team. Swift, agile, powerful, and loyal, **kaadu** are beloved by their Gungan masters for their steadfast endurance. These creatures evolved in the Naboo swamps and possess sharp hearing and a keen sense of smell.

KAADU

OPEE SEA KILLER

The **opee sea killer,** a nasty, multi-legged crustacean, has luminescent spots and resides in the ocean depths of Naboo. The creature snags unlucky victims with a lightning-fast adhesive tongue and shreds them in its powerful, sharp-toothed maw.

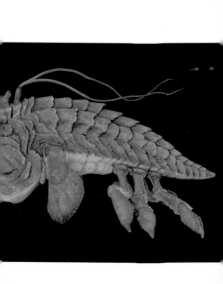

Sando Aqua Monster

Fearsome ruler of the deep, Naboo's **sando aqua monster** is a snake-bodied leviathan with snapping jaws and an unquenchable appetite. Constantly eating

in order to maintain its bulk, the
enormous eel inhales whole schools of
small fish and is always prowling for
larger, meatier morsels.

To surprise its prey and to protect itself from Naboo's larger ocean predators, the crafty **colo claw fish** dwells in hidden tunnels along the sea floor. This spine-studded beast can lie perfectly still for hours, then suddenly explode into motion and seize a passing meal in its hooked claws.

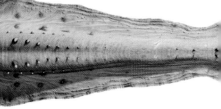

COLO CLAW FISH

Eopie

The **eopie** is a common sight on the sun-baked world of Tatooine. These hardy quadrupeds are acclimated to the heat of the unprotected desert and are employed by local colonists as mounts and pack animals. Though slow, eopies are dependable and can survive for weeks on very little water.

FAMBAA

Hulking and more than a little clumsy, **fambaas** are sluggish Naboo swamp lizards notorious for their puny brains. Though they are slow to obey even the simplest orders, fambaas have thick scaly hides that can take a beating, making them the perfect conveyances for carrying Gungan shield generators into battle.

Gungans know that **falumpasets** are the strongest hauling beasts on all of Naboo, which is why they are willing to put up with the creatures' ornery temperaments.

Highly intelligent, falumpasets are used to haul energy-ball ammo wagons and convey high-ranking Gungan leaders.

Falumpaset

Hyperactive and often quite comical, **nunas** are solitary omnivores that band together each season in vast sweeping migrations to the wettest Naboo swamplands. Nunas will always flee in the face of danger, but if cornered will lash out with frantic kicks from their powerful legs.

NUNA

PEKO
PEKO

The **peko peko** is a Naboo swamp bird with an appetite for toxic jute nuts, which they crack open with their powerful hooked beaks. Peko peko blood contains a natural anti-venom that is used in Gungan folk medicine, making the birds valuable prizes for Gungan hunters.

Shaak

The shambling mammals known as **shaaks** are herbivores that roam the Naboo plains in search of tasty grasses and flowers. Shaaks are a valuable food source for the Gungans and the Naboo.

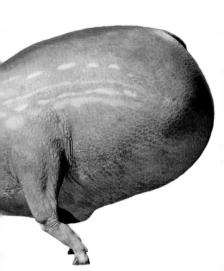

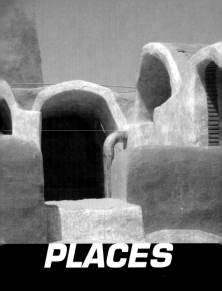

PLACES

THEED ROYAL PALACE

Queen Amidala of Naboo addresses the needs of her people from the **Theed Royal Palace**, an ancient and beautiful structure adorned with creeping ivy and ornamented statues. Although the peaceful Naboo have no standing army, the palace is not far from a starfighter launch hangar for the volunteer security forces.

Few visitors ever venture underwater to **Otoh Gunga**, but those who do are awed by the eerie organic beauty of the Gungan capital. Some of the city's multi-leveled bubbles are over 75 meters tall. Permeable hydrostatic membranes keep seawater at bay, but still allow individuals to enter and leave.

OTOH GUNGA

MOS ESPA ARENA

With room for more than 100,000 spectators, the colossal **Mos Espa Arena** dominates an expanse of Tatooine

desert lying near Metta Drop and the Old Town ruins. Construction of the grandstand was financed by the Hutts, who made a fortune by instituting organized gambling on the Podraces.

Watto's Junk Shop

The merchant district of Mos Espa contains dozens of barter markets, including a dilapidated scrapheap owned by a winged Toydarian named Watto. Behind the shop's adobe storefront lies a courtyard littered with mechanical parts—everything from a case of spare astromech flywheels to a fully-functional T-14 hyperdrive unit.

*T*he slave trade, banned on most civilized planets, is alive and well on lawless Tatooine. Anakin Skywalker and his mother live in a warren-like complex of slave dwellings located on the outskirts of Mos Espa. Implanted subdermal transmitters keep track of their every move.

SLAVE QUARTERS

JEDI TEMPLE

The slender, graceful spire that crowns the **Jedi Temple** stands out like a celestial beacon among the blocky ferrocrete skyscrapers of Coruscant. Inside, the Council members sit on simple chairs as they conduct business.

Jedi Council Chamber

Within the tower's walls lies the **Jedi Council Chamber**, where the twelve members of the Jedi Council meet to discuss galactic events and to test new initiates.

Galactic Senate Chamber

One of the most breathtaking sights on all of Coruscant, the **Galactic Senate Chamber**'s cavernous amphitheater houses thousands of senators from every world in the Galactic Republic. When a delegation wishes to speak, its platform floats to a position in front of the Supreme Chancellor's central dais.

This book has been bound using handcraft
methods and Smyth-sewn to ensure durability.

The dust jacket was designed by
Toni Renée Leslie

The interior was designed by
Maria Taffera Lewis

All film stills and photographic materials
are from the Lucasfilm Archives,
coordinated by Matthew Azeveda.

The text was edited by
Marc Frey and Allan Kausch

The text was set in Eurostile Condensed

Herrings Potted in Irish Stout

Micky Gill's Beef
Braised with Irish Stout

Spare Ribs with Irish Stout

Sirloin Steak Marinated
in Irish Stout

Steak and Irish Stout Pie

Spiced Beef Marinated
in Irish Stout

Lentils with Irish Stout

St Patrick's Stout Jelly

Aunty Betty's
Christmas Pudding

Porter Cake

Irish Oysters with Irish Stout

Stuffed Mussels

SERVES 4-6

48 large mussels
300 ml / ½ pt / 1¼ cups Irish stout
225 g / 8 oz / 1 cup butter, at room temperature
10 cloves of garlic, crushed
110 g / 4 oz / 2 cups fresh breadcrumbs
handful of fresh parsley, chopped
1 lemon, cut in wedges

Prepare the mussels by scraping off barnacles and pulling off the hairy beards, under running water. Discard any that are broken or that refuse to close when tapped. Place the mussels in a pan with the stout and a little water and steam them open. Drain and remove top shell. Combine the butter and crushed garlic and mix well with the breadcrumbs. Add chopped parsley. Place some of the mixture on each mussel and grill under a high heat for 5-10 minutes until sizzling. Serve with lemon wedges and crusty bread.

Herrings Potted in Irish Stout

SERVES 4

4 fresh herrings, filleted
1 medium onion, cut in rings
1 tsp salt
1 bay leaf
4 cloves
6 white peppercorns
6 black peppercorns
1 tsp sugar
150 ml / ¼ pt / ¾ cup Irish stout
150 ml / ¼ pt / ¾ cup white malt vinegar

Heat the oven to 160°C/325°F/Gas 3. Roll up fillets from tail end and arrange side by side, with seam underneath, in a casserole dish. Arrange the onion rings, salt, bay leaf, spices and sugar over the fish. Mix stout and vinegar and pour over the fish. Cover and cook in the oven for 50 minutes. Turn the oven off and leave for 2 hours.

Transfer to a serving dish and spoon over some of the liquid.

Serve cold. (If left overnight in the fridge, the stock will set to a jelly.)

Micky Gill's Beef Braised with Irish Stout

SERVES 4

2 tblsp olive oil
2 bay leaves
1¼ kg / 2¾ lb well-hung stewing beef, cut into
1 cm / ½ in pieces
1 large onion, sliced
1 medium clove of garlic, crushed
2 tblsp seasoned flour
150 ml / ¼ pt / ¾ cup Irish stout
225 g / 8 oz carrots, sliced in 1 cm / ½ in pieces
110 g / 4 oz mushrooms, sliced
salt and pepper
1 bouquet garni or ½ tsp dried mixed herbs
1 tblsp fresh parsley, chopped

Heat the olive oil in a casserole dish and add
bay leaves. Add beef and brown quickly.
Remove beef from dish and set aside. Soften
onion and garlic in the oil. Return beef to
casserole, sprinkle in seasoned flour, let it
brown, then add stout and enough cold
water just to cover the meat. Add the carrots
and mushrooms, season with salt and
pepper. Bring to the boil, then add the
bouquet garni or mixed herbs. Cover and
braise in a slow oven (160°C/325°F/Gas 3)
for about 1½ hours until tender. Add more
liquid if required. To serve, remove bay
leaves and sprinkle with chopped parsley.

Spare Ribs with Irish Stout

SERVES 4

1 kg / 2½ lb pork or beef spare ribs
600 ml / 1 pt / 2½ cups Irish stout
50 g / 2 oz / ¼ cup sugar
salt and pepper
juice of ½ lemon
sprig of fresh rosemary
1 tblsp tomato ketchup
Glaze: 5 tblsp each of Irish stout and maple syrup, and 2 tblsp lemon juice mixed together

Place the meat in a shallow container with a lid. Combine all the other ingredients (except the glaze) and pour over the meat. Cover with the lid and place container overnight in the fridge.

Pre-heat the oven to 220°C/425°F/Gas 7. Place the meat in a large piece of foil in a roasting pan and baste with the marinade. Bake for 1 hour. Remove from the oven, open the foil and brush the meat with the glaze of Irish stout, syrup and lemon juice. Grill under a medium heat for 10 minutes each side.

Sirloin Steak Marinated in Irish Stout

SERVES 4

*4 sirloin steaks approx. 300 g / 10 oz each and
approx. 3 cm / 1¼ in thick
300 ml / ½ pt / 1¼ cups Irish stout
300 ml / ½ pt / 1¼ cups chicken stock
pinch of fresh thyme
1 tsp Worcestershire sauce
1 bay leaf
1 tsp freshly ground pepper
75 g / 3 oz / 6 tblsp butter, cut in pieces
salt to taste*

Make a marinade with the Irish stout, stock,
thyme, Worcestershire sauce and bay leaf in a

casserole dish. Add the meat
and season with half the
pepper. Cover and leave for
about 8 hours, turning the
meat once or twice. Remove the steaks from
the marinade, pat dry and sprinkle with more
pepper. Heat the marinade in a medium
saucepan over a fairly high heat until the
liquid has been reduced by half. Skim off
any scum that rises to the surface. Strain
the marinade mixture into a clean saucepan.
Grill the steaks as required, turning once.
Reheat the sauce gently but do not boil.
Whisk the butter into the sauce, one piece
at a time. Add salt to taste. Serve the steak
with a little sauce poured over and the
rest handed separately.

Steak and Irish Stout Pie

SERVES 4

*900 g / 2 lb best quality beef steak,
cut into small pieces
1 tblsp seasoned flour
75 g / 3 oz / 6 tblsp butter
8 rashers of bacon, chopped small
5 onions, chopped
1 tblsp raisins
1 tsp brown sugar
300 ml / ½ pt / 1¼ cups Irish stout
450-675 g / 1-1½ lb shortcrust pastry
beaten egg to glaze*

Roll the meat in seasoned flour and brown in
butter with the bacon pieces. Place all the
meat in a casserole dish. Fry the onions in
butter until golden and add to the meat. Add
the raisins, brown sugar and Irish stout.
Cover tightly and simmer very gently for
about 2 hours, until the meat is tender. Stir
now and then, and add a little more stout or
water if necessary.
Transfer all to a deep
pie dish and cover
with a layer of pastry.
Brush the pastry with
beaten egg and cook
in a hot oven (200°C/400°F/Gas 6)
until golden brown, about
30-35 minutes.

Spiced Beef Marinated in Irish Stout

SERVES 6-8

1.35-1.8 kg / 3-4 lb piece of spiced beef
600 ml / 1 pt / 2½ cups Irish stout
1 onion, sliced
1 carrot, sliced
2 sticks of celery, finely sliced
1 small turnip, finely chopped
1 tsp allspice (optional)

Place the beef in a large bowl with the stout. Add enough cold water to cover the meat and leave for 24 hours. Remove the meat from bowl and place in large pan with the vegetables and allspice. Cover with cold water. Bring to the boil and simmer gently for about 1 hour. Drain off the liquid, discard the vegetables and transfer to a roasting tin in a pre-heated oven (180°C/350°F/Gas 4). Cook for 30 minutes.

Lentils with Irish Stout

SERVES 4

250 g / 9 oz / 1 cup red lentils, soaked for
3 hours, then drained
600 ml / 1 pt / 2 ½ cups Irish stout
generous dash of balsamic vinegar
50 g / 2 oz / ¼ cup brown sugar
1½ tsp salt
pinch of freshly ground pepper
3 carrots, finely sliced
1 medium leek, sliced
handful of fresh parsley, chopped

Put the lentils and Irish stout in a
saucepan and add the vinegar, sugar, salt,
pepper, carrots and leek. Bring to the boil
and boil rapidly over high heat
for 15-20 minutes until the
liquid is reduced.
Delicious served
with roast
meat and
potatoes.

St Patrick's Stout Jelly

SERVES 4

gelatine (to stiffen 600 ml /1 pt /2½ cups water)
300 ml / ½ pt / 1¼ cups strong coffee
300 ml / ½ pt / 1¼ cups Irish stout
packet of green jelly
generous dash of Baileys Irish Cream
300 ml / ½ pt / 1¼ cups double cream,
lightly whipped
75 g / 3 oz / ⅓ cup brown sugar
small tin of mandarin oranges

Soak the gelatine in 5 tblsp of cold water
for 5 minutes. Add to the coffee and stout

mixture in a small
saucepan and heat
gently while stirring.
Do not allow to boil.
Pour into 4 glass dessert
dishes. Prepare the green
jelly as instructed and
pour into a flat, rectangular dish. Leave
both mixtures overnight in the fridge.
Next day, chop the green jelly in small
pieces and place on top of the coffee and
stout jelly. Add the Baileys to the lightly
whipped cream and pour over the jelly
mixture. Sprinkle with brown sugar
and decorate with slices of drained
mandarin oranges.

Aunty Betty's Christmas Pudding

SERVES 6-8

110 g / 4 oz / 1½ cups sultanas
225 g / 8 oz / 3 cups currants
110 g / 4 oz / 1½ cups candied peel, chopped
50 g / 2 oz / ⅓ cup blanched almonds, chopped
2 sharp apples, peeled and grated or chopped
110 g / 4 oz / 1 cup flour
225 g / 8 oz / 5 cups soft breadcrumbs
225 g / 8 oz / 1 cup beef suet
225 g / 8 oz / 1 cup brown sugar
1 tsp mixed spice, ½ tsp salt
5-6 eggs, beaten together
grated rind and juice of 1 lemon or orange
300 ml / ½ pt / 1¼ cups Irish stout

Place all the prepared fruit in a large basin with other dry ingredients and mix well. Add beaten eggs, lemon or orange juice and stout and bind all together. Leave overnight. Turn into a well-greased pudding bowl (1 litre/ 2 pt size) and cover with greaseproof paper. Steam or boil gently for 4 hours, making sure the water does not evaporate. Leave to cool, then wrap well in greaseproof paper and store in a tin for several weeks. Steam or boil gently for 2 hours before serving. Just before bringing to table, pour over a little Irish whiskey and ignite. Serve with brandy butter.

Porter Cake

225 g / 8 oz / 1 cup butter
225 g / 8 oz / 1 cup brown sugar
300 ml / ½ pt / 1¼ cups Irish stout
225 g / 8 oz / 1 cup raisins
225 g / 8 oz / 1 cup sultanas
110 g / 4 oz / ½ cup mixed peel
450 g / 1 lb / 4 cups plain flour
½ tsp bicarbonate of soda
½ tsp allspice
½ tsp ground nutmeg
110 g / 4 oz / ½ cup glacé cherries, rinsed,
dried and chopped in half
grated rind of 1 lemon
3 medium eggs, whisked together

Melt the butter and sugar with the stout over a low heat. Add the dried fruit (except for the cherries) and bring to the boil. Simmer for 10 minutes. Allow to cool, then add the

sieved flour, soda and spices to the mixture. Add the cherries and lemon rind, then slowly add the whisked eggs. Mix well. Pour into a greased and lined 25cm/9in tin. Bake in the middle of a pre-heated oven (180°C/350°F/Gas 4) for about 1½ hours. The cake is ready when a skewer inserted in the centre comes out clean. Leave to cool in the tin.